The Creative Toddler's

First
COLORING
BOOK

ISBN: 9798701873146 (US Edition)
For questions and suggestions please contact us at
imagipreschool@gmail.com

D1309351

Puppy

Balloon

Puzzle

Ball

Train

Car

Teddy Bear

Blocks

Kite

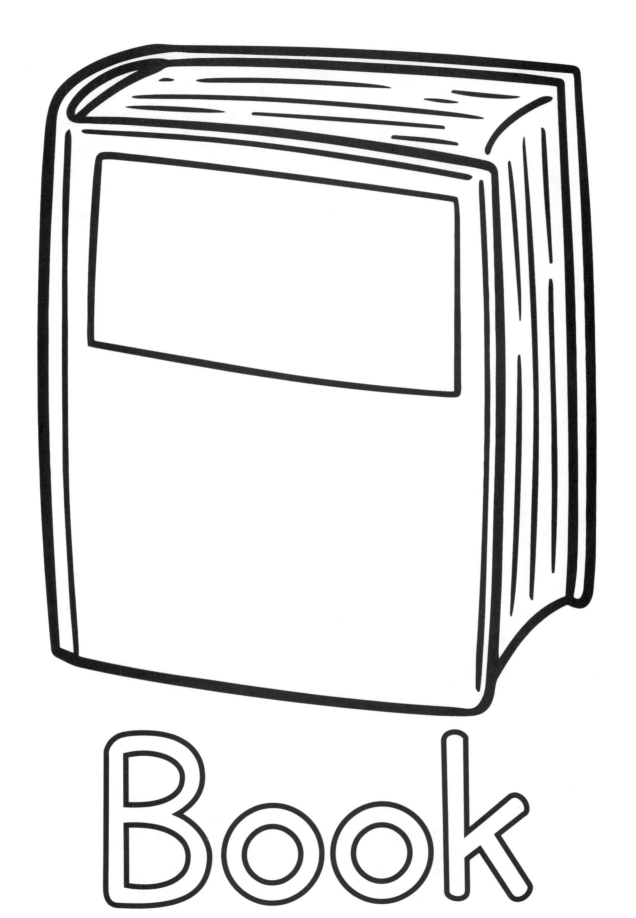

Book

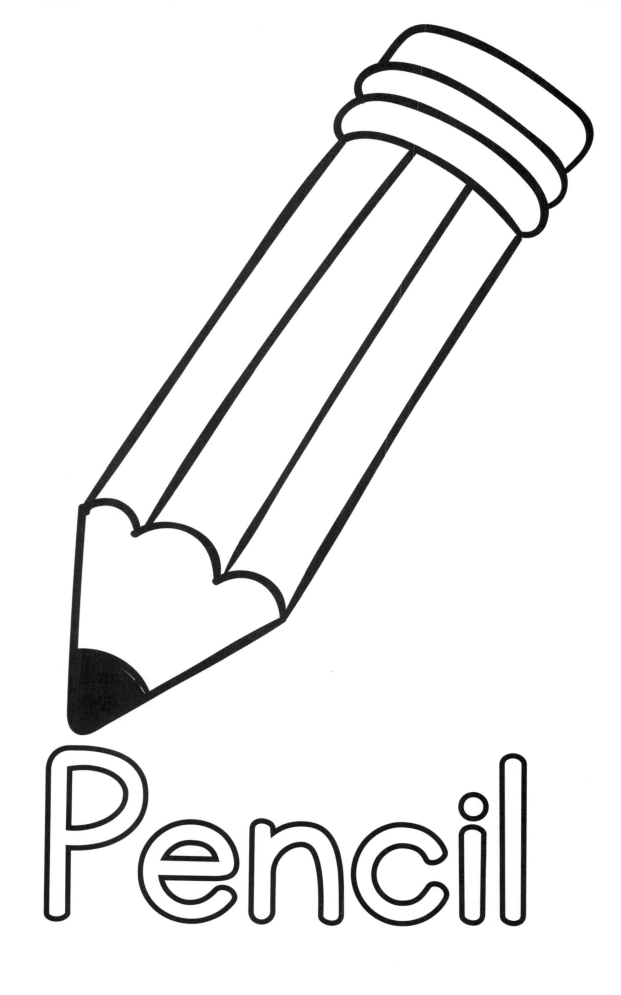

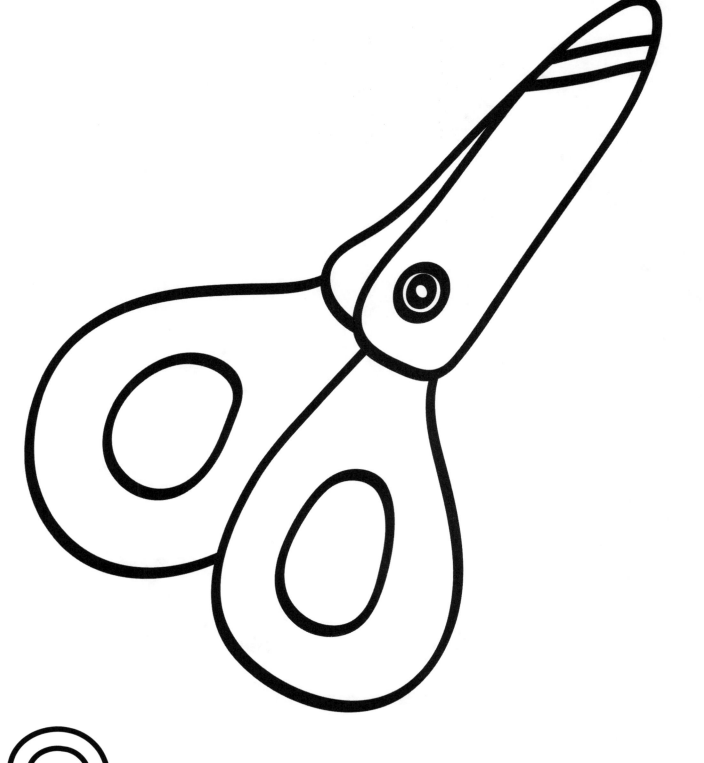

Scissors

Shoes

Socks

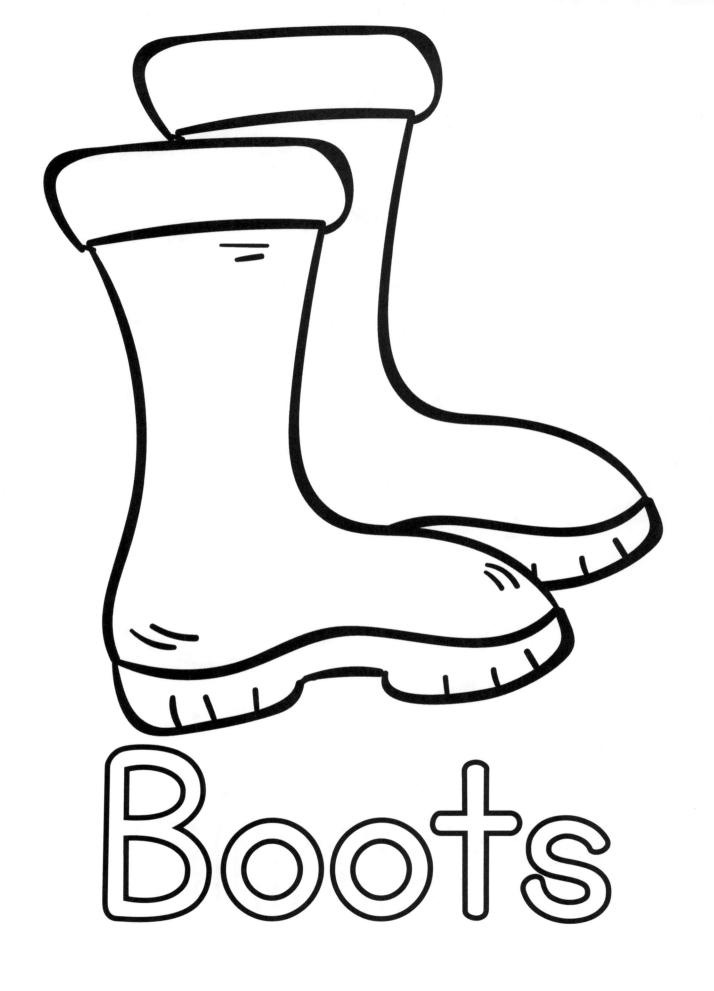

Boots

T-shirt

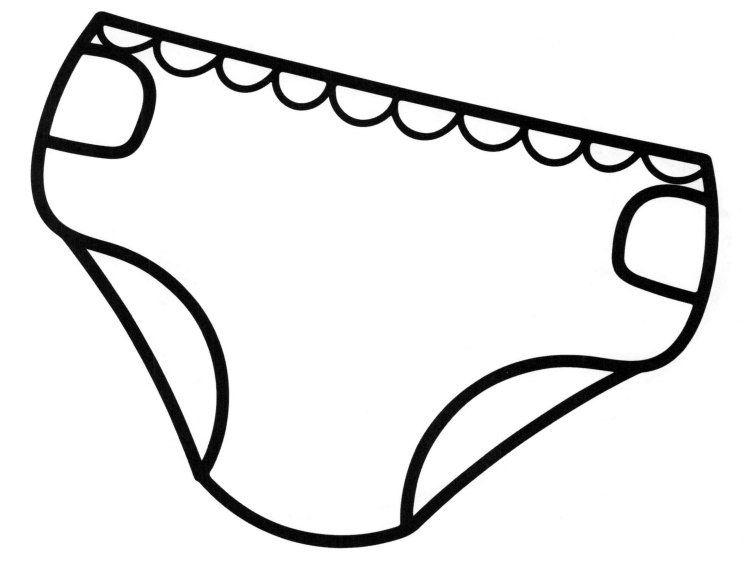

Underwear

Hat

Umbrella

Glove

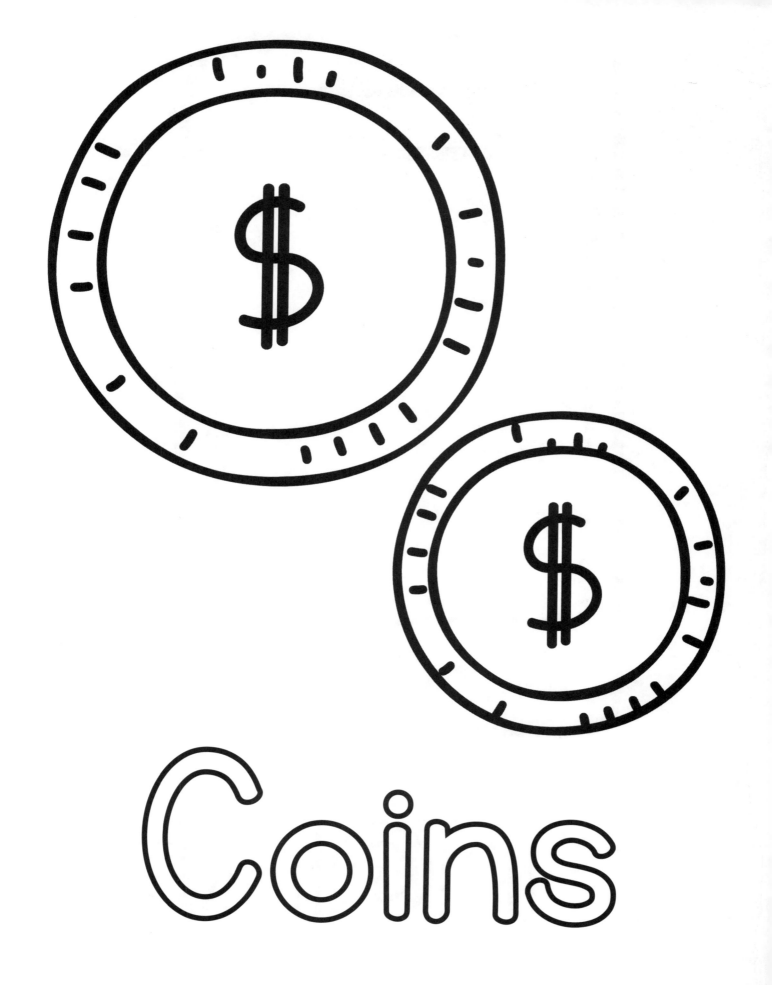

Coins

Phone

Cup

Bucket

Spoon
fork

Pear

Strawberry

Banana

Cherry

Watermelon

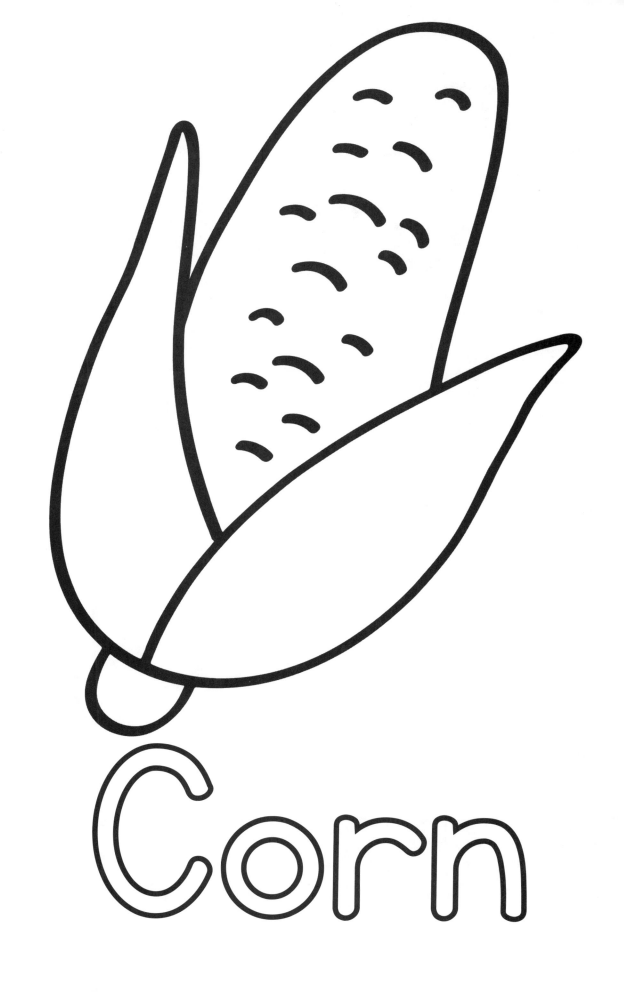

Corn

Carrot

Tomato

Pumpkin

Broccoli

Lemon

Icecream

Cake

Candy

Sun

Star

Cloud

Leaf

Flower

Mushroom

Farm

Dog

Cow

Chick

Sheep

Goat

Horse

Donkey

Rabbit

Duck

Goose

Mouse

Bees

Bug

Butterfly

Bird

Turtle

Owl

Frog

Snail

Hedgehog

Bat

Squirrel

Lion

Elephant

Giraffe

Zebra

Leopard

Hippo

Rhino

Gorilla

Bear

Alligator

Monkey

Snake

Deer

Parrot

Swan

Dolphin

Penguin

Seal